Melissa E. Vallas M.D.
Illustrated by
Terri Cooper

God has a Plan for Me

To: Sterling
Always Remember

Dr. Julia

Vallas Publications
Dublin, CA 94568
Melissavallasmd.com

Printed in the United States of America

Cover & Interior Design: Terri Cooper

Photographer: Andrea Kiefer

Editor: Christine Gomez

Graphic Designer: Karen Davis

Publisher: Vallas Publications

Art and Design by: Terri Cooper

To: Kelly, Michael, and Mia

Always remember...

God has a plan for me,
Something much bigger than I can see.

It's higher than a mountain,
Taller than a tree,

Farther than the sky,
And as deep as the sea.

It's God's special plan made just for me,
To help me become all I can be.
All I have to do is trust and believe
Something amazing is waiting for me!

No matter what other people may say,
With God nothing can get in my way.

So when friends hurt my feelings and make me sad
Or when I am in trouble because I've been bad,
There is one thing I still believe;
I believe that my God has a plan for me.

When I am afraid and I think I will fail
Or when I am hurting and have no one to tell,
There is one thing I still believe;
I believe that my God has a plan for me.

When I look at how God planned the world around me—
The mountains, the trees, the sky, the sea,
There is one thing I clearly see;
How beautiful God's plan for me must be!

A Note to Parents:

Equipping our children with key personal resources that promote optimism and resiliency are crucial for their development. This book celebrates a child's sense of purpose. Purpose involves awareness that life holds unique meaning and value. A strong sense of purpose can promote optimism and strengthen resiliency, often leading to a better sense of direction. Children with purpose tend to believe they can make a difference and be successful even when faced with circumstances that may suggest otherwise. Undoubtedly, a child's earnest belief that their life has purpose is a powerful resource.

My hope is that every time you read this book to your child, you are reminded that your child's life has a purpose and that you have a role in helping them to fulfill it. Take the time to engage your child in conversations that begin to provoke their thinking about the uniqueness and value of their life. Encourage your child to believe in themselves. You could start by asking, "What do you think God has planned for you?" or "What do you hope for your life?"

Dr. Melissa E. Vallas

Dr. Melissa Vallas is a Stanford University trained child psychiatrist. She is a Diplomate of the Board of Psychiatry and Neurology, holding board certifications in both general and child & adolescent psychiatry. She has years of experience working with children who suffer with mental health disorders ranging from mild to extremely severe.

Dr. Vallas has dedicated her personal career to treating children with mental illness and improving those systems of care within her community that provide services to children who are disadvantaged and under-served. She currently practices psychiatry in the San Francisco Bay Area where she lives with her husband and their three young children. Her writing is inspired by her experience as a mother and by her work with children in her practice. She combines her training with her faith and her personal and professional experiences to create magical and playful stories that are geared toward helping children gain a deeper understanding of themselves and the world around them.

34256708R00015

Made in the USA
Charleston, SC
01 October 2014